KILLER

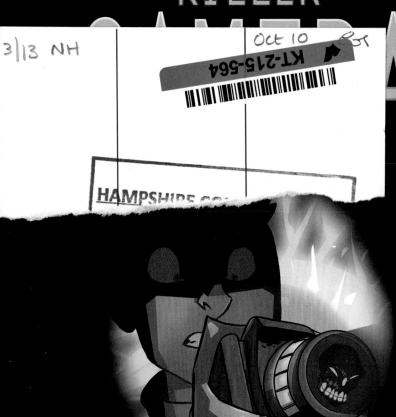

ANTHONY HOROWITZ

ADAPTED BY TONY LEE • ILLUSTRATED BY DAN BOULTWOOD

First published in 2010
by Franklin Watts

Text © Franklin Watts 2010
Based on the original short story KILLER CAMERA
Original text © Anthony Horowitz 1999
Illustrations © Dan Boultwood 2010
Cover design by Peter Scoulding

Franklin Watts
338 Euston Road
London NW1 3BH

Franklin Watts Australia
Level 17/207 Kent Street
Sydney, NSW 2000

A CIP catalogue record for this book
is available from the British Library.

ISBN: 978 0 7496 9510 1

1   3   5   7   9   10   8   6   4   2

Printed in China

Franklin Watts is a division of Hachette Children's Books

Hey - that's **twelve weeks** of shoe cleaning, car washing - and generally helping around the house!

That's everything I have - and I'm not going to spend it all in a **crummy Crouch End car boot sale!**

I'll just have to go into **London** and see if I can find something for Dad in a **sale** -

- hold on. **Late entry.** And he doesn't look like the **usual** seller of second-hand goods.

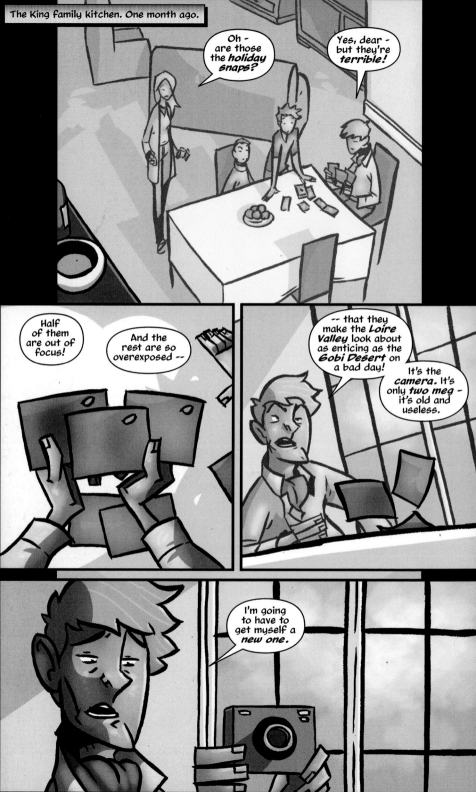

The King family kitchen.

It must be **stolen,** Matthew!

I don't **think** so - I told you what he said!

How much did you **pay** for it?

None of your **business,** Jamie!

Oh look! There's a **memory card** in here!

Maybe you should see if there's anything on it!

POP!

It could be **porn!** I could check it on my computer right now!

Grow up, moron! It's probably just boring family snaps!

Nerd!

Wimp!

Come on boys, let's not fight - it's a nice present. Dad will love it.

And he doesn't need to know where you got it - just wipe the memory card. That's easy to do, right?

14

It was *quick*, Matthew. And the driver took Polonius's body to the vet.

He's going to be *cremated*.

Polonius is *gone!* I'm so sorry!

He's been part of the family since he was a *puppy* — and now he's *gone!*

You took a *picture* of him.

That *picture* is all we have left.

Where are you going?

I've just remembered something *important* that I have to do!

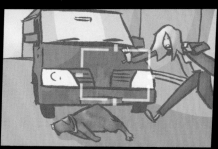

CLICK!

Everything we take a photo of either **breaks** or **dies**. And it's your fault.

So... if I can't get you working on my computer --

-- let's see what happens when I take you to a *professional*.

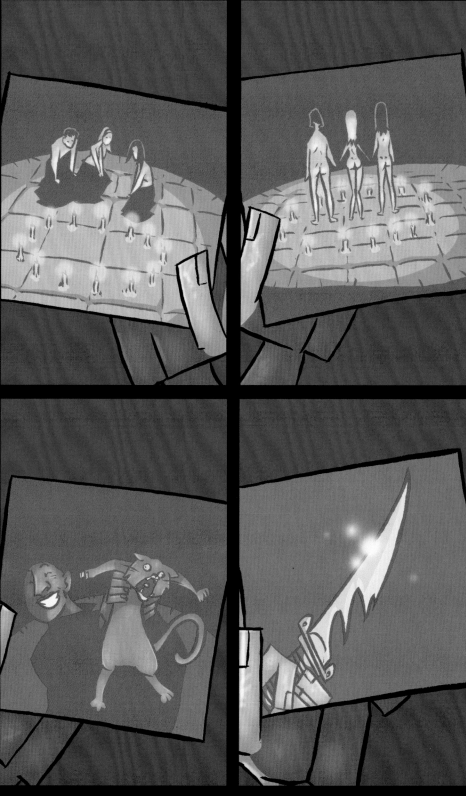

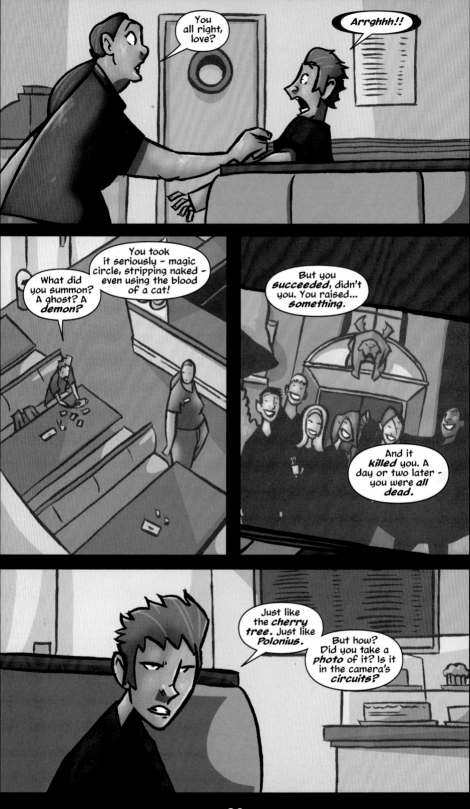

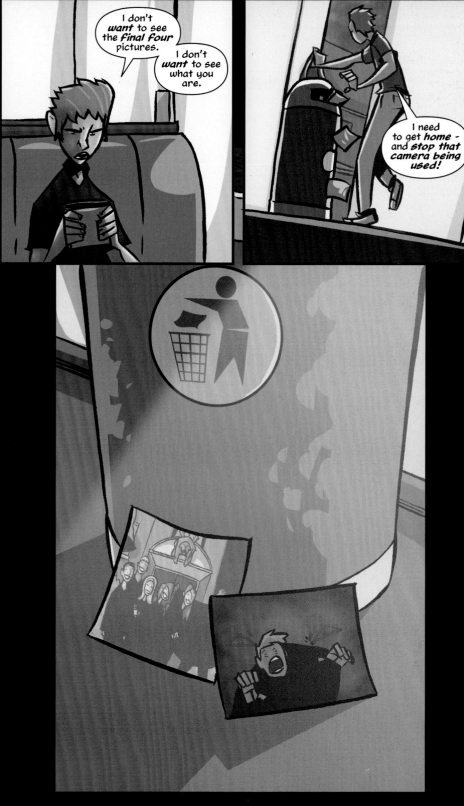

"They disappeared. Just did a bunk..."

Mum! Dad! Jamie! Where *are* you?

Find the camera. *Smash* the camera.

I'll explain it to Dad later.

Then again - maybe not.

'You see Dad, this *guy* had the camera and he used it in some kind of *black magic ritual*.'

'He took a picture of a *demon* - and it either *killed* him or *frightened him away*.'

'And now it's *inside the camera* and every time you take a picture, you *kill* whatever you're aiming at.'

Yeah. He'll think that I'm *mad*. Best *not* to explain.

I could throw it into the bottom of a canal, then say it was *stolen* --

The sun had *disappeared,* and Matthew stood watching as the clouds *closed in –*

London!

I took a picture of *all of London!*

– and the *darkness* rolled towards the city...

End.

ANTHONY HOROWITZ

Anthony's mum used to read him horror stories when he was eight years old, and this is the inevitable result. He has been called the busiest writer in England and is best known for his ALEX RIDER novels which have sold over twelve million copies worldwide. He used to write in a garden shed until his wife sold the garden. Now he lives and works in London.

TONY LEE

Tony has been writing for over twenty years, and has worked on X-MEN, SPIDER MAN and recently DOCTOR WHO for IDW. His graphic novel OUTLAW: THE LEGEND OF ROBIN HOOD for Walker Books was on the ALA 'Best of 2010' list. Tony is also adapting Anthony Horowitz's POWER OF FIVE series for Walker Books.

DAN BOULTWOOD

Dan has illustrated several critically acclaimed graphic novels, including THE GLOOM and HOPE FALLS for Markosia, THE PRINCE OF BAGHDAD for Random House and G.P. Taylor's THE DOPPLEGANGER CHRONICLES for Tyndale Press.

KILLER CAMERA by Anthony Horowitz was originally published by Orchard Books. Check out all the frightfully good HOROWITZ HORROR titles at: www.orchardbooks.co.uk

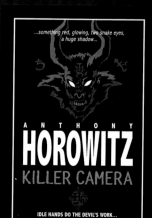

...something red, glowing, two snake eyes, a huge shadow...

ANTHONY

HOROWITZ
KILLER CAMERA

IDLE HANDS DO THE DEVIL'S WORK...

Other HOROWITZ GRAPHIC HORROR titles:

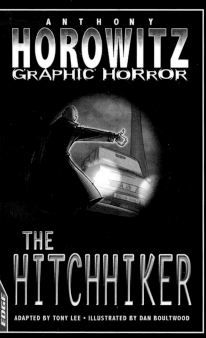

THE **HITCHHIKER**

ADAPTED BY TONY LEE • ILLUSTRATED BY DAN BOULTWOOD

978 0 7496 9512 5

THE PHONE GOES **DEAD**

ADAPTED BY TONY LEE • ILLUSTRATED BY DAN BOULTWOOD

978 0 7496 9509 5

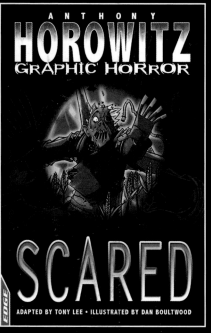

SCARED

ADAPTED BY TONY LEE • ILLUSTRATED BY DAN BOULTWOOD

978 0 7496 9511 8